DECLARATION OF THE RIGHTS OF BOYS

First published in 2014 in French under the title *La déclaration des droits des garçons* by Talents Hauts, France

This English edition first published in 2017 by
Little Island Books
7 Kenilworth Park
Dublin 6W
Ireland

© Talents Hauts 2014

Translation © Little Island Books 2017

ISBN: 978-1-910411-27-8

A British Library Cataloguing in Publication record for this book is available from the British Library

Printed in Poland by Drukarnia Skleniarz

Little Island receives financial assistance from The Arts Council/An Chomhairle Ealaíon

Little Island acknowledges the financial support of Literature Ireland for the translation of this book and for their ongoing support of translation in Ireland

This book is endorsed by Amnesty International Ireland (www.amnesty.ie)

10 9 8 7 6 5 4 3 2 1

Declaration of the Rights of Boys

Élisabeth Brami
Estelle Billon-Spagnol

Little Island

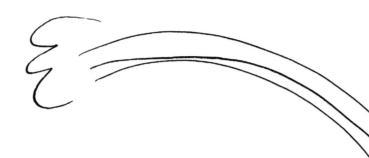

Boys have just as much right as girls to do the stuff they like. They have:

ARTICLE 1

The right to cry and to be hugged

me
me
me

NAH

I'm not crying

Muuum Muuuum
Mum Mum Mum
Mum

Not AGAIN?

ARTICLE 2

The right to be clean, sweet-smelling, stylish, cutesy, quiet and well-behaved – picture-perfect

ARTICLE 3

The right to play with dolls,
at tea-parties, mummies-and-daddies,
skipping, hopscotch ...

ARTICLE 4

The right to be good at
reading and writing
and not ace at maths

ARTICLE 5

The right to be no good at DIY or hammering a nail and the right to hate getting their hands dirty

ARTICLE 6

The right to wear pink, yellow,
purple and all the colours of the rainbow

ARTICLE 7

The right to do any job they like:
creche-worker, school-teacher, dancer,
nurse, midwife, housekeeper ...

ARTICLE 8

The right to learn
ballet, flute or harp

ARTICLE 9

The right to read love stories, poetry,
fairy tales, and the right to
cry in the cinema

The right to be a bit shy and scared,
not to like fighting and not to be muscly,
without being called a sissy

ARTICLE 11

The right to learn how to sew, to knit, to iron and to tidy up

The right to wipe a baby's nose, change its nappy and look after it

Shhh!
i think he's asleep
POP
and then Mrs Tomato comes along
blah blah blah blah
blah
WAAH
WAAH
WAAH
WAAH
WAAH
Go to sleep
You'll get cake – chocolate cake
Give a big blow

ARTICLE **13**

The right to have long hair,
a pony tail, braids, dreadlocks ...

ARTICLE 14

The right not to be a superhero
every day

ARTICLE 15

The right to fall in love with anyone they like: girl or boy or both

For André Nahum, a free man – E. Brami

You will see the Amnesty logo on the cover of this book. That means that Amnesty International supports this 'declaration', which debunks received ideas and stereotypes – a quirky list of invented rights, which reminds us how important it is to value equality for all.

For Irena Milewska, a free woman – E. Brami

You will see the Amnesty logo on the cover of this book. That means that Amnesty International supports this 'declaration', which debunks received ideas and stereotypes – a quirky list of invented rights, which reminds us how important it is to value equality for all.

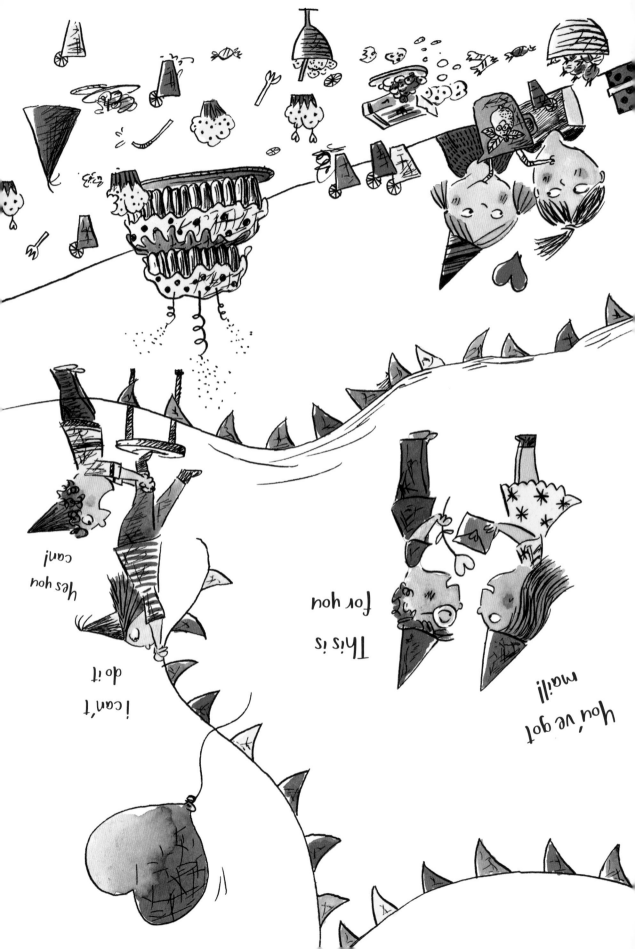

ARTICLE **15**

The right to fall in love with anyone
they like: boy, girl or both

The right not to be a princess every day

ARTICLE 13

The right to have really short hair

ARTICLE 12

The right to be disgusted when changing
a baby or wiping its nose

ARTICLE 11

The right not to like sewing, knitting or tidying up

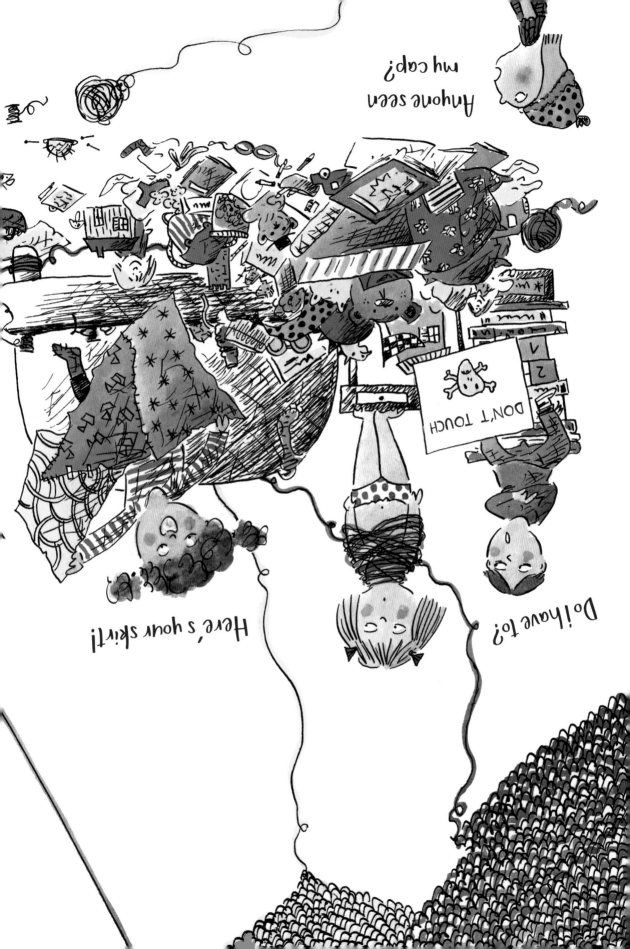

ARTICLE 10

The right to yell, stand up for
themselves, fight, lose their temper,
without being called a tomboy

ARTICLE 9

The right to read crime novels,
adventure stories, horror stories,
and to like scary movies

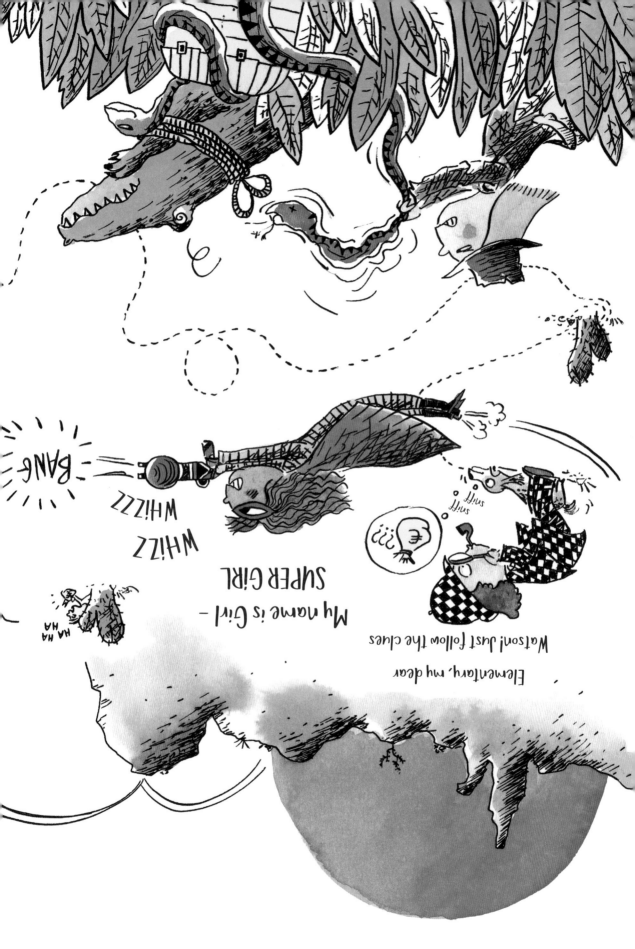

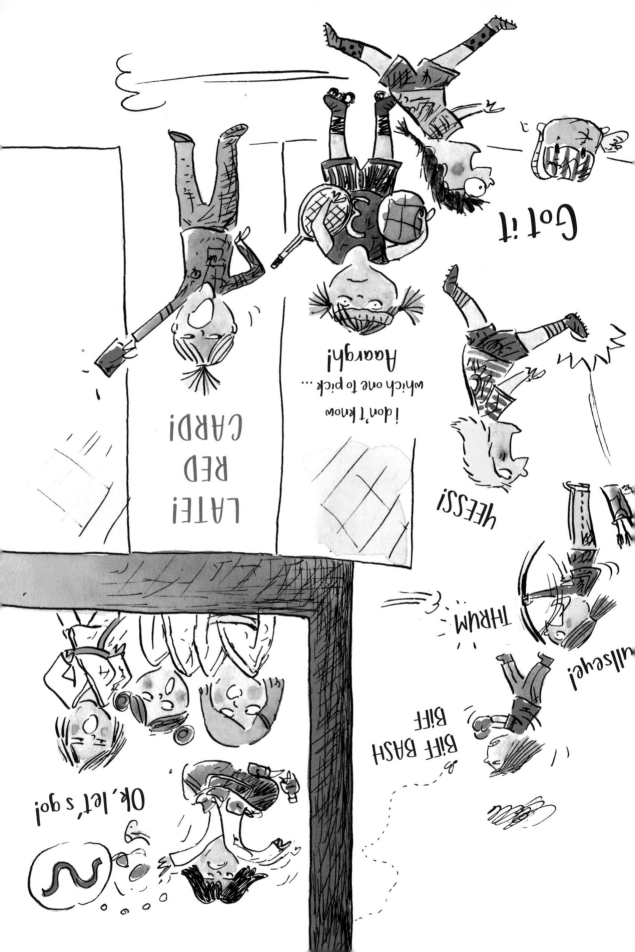

ARTICLE 8

The right to learn judo, archery, boxing, football, fencing ...

ARTICLE 7

The right to do any job they like:
lorry driver, astronaut, police chief,
judge, factory manager, president,
sculptor, surgeon ...

* I want to get out of here too!

ARTICLE 6

The right to wear blue, black, khaki and all the colours of the rainbow

us

us again

The right to wear trainers, hoodies, dungarees, shorts, baseball caps ...

ARTICLE 4

The right to climb trees, build forts, scramble over fences …

ARTICLE 3

The right to be good at maths
and not so great at English

ARTICLE 2

The right to play marbles, play with cars, rockets, train sets, and to play video games

Girls have just as much right as boys to do the stuff they like. They have:

The right to be untidy, scruffy, covered in scratches, hyper ...

Wheeeeee!

Hee

Elisabeth Brami
Estelle Billon-Spagnol

Declaration of the Rights of Girls

DECLARATION OF THE RIGHTS OF GIRLS

First published in 2014 in French under the title *La déclaration des droits des filles* by Talents Hauts, France

This English edition first published in 2017 by

Little Island Books

7 Kenilworth Park

Dublin 6W

Ireland

© Talents Hauts 2014

Translation © Little Island Books 2017

ISBN: 978-1-910411-27-8

A British Library Cataloguing in Publication record for this book is available from the British Library

Printed in Poland by Drukarnia Skleniarz

Little Island receives financial assistance from The Arts Council/An Chomhairle Ealaíon

Little Island acknowledges the financial support of Literature Ireland for the translation of this book and for their ongoing support of translation in Ireland

This book is endorsed by Amnesty International Ireland (www.amnesty.ie)

10 9 8 7 6 5 4 3 2 1

This book should be returned to any branch of the
Lancashire County Library on or before the date shown

		0 6 APR 2019